Gitarre • Guitar

16 Momentaufnahmen

16 Snapshots

Rainer Schrecklinger

UNTERWEGS

On the Road

RICORDI

2723

IMPRESSUM

© 2019 by G. RICORDI & CO. Bühnen- und Musikverlag GmbH, Berlin (für alle Länder)

Alle Rechte vorbehalten | All rights reserved

Notensatz | Engraving: Matteo Pennese

ISMN 979-0-2042-2723-5

Inhalt | Index

Unterwegs
16 Momentaufnahmen

Nach einer Reise zehrt man noch lange von all den Erinnerungen, Erlebnissen, Begegnungen mit Menschen und Eindrücken von faszinierenden Lebewesen und Landschaften. Die Kompositionen in dieser Notenausgabe sind hörbare Momentaufnahmen. Bei jeder einzelnen habe ich mich an ein ganz bestimmtes Bild, Erlebnis oder Gefühl während einer meiner Reisen zurückerinnert und es in Klänge umgedeutet.

Zudem sind die Stücke dazu geeignet, essenzielle Dreifingerarpeggios der rechten Hand einzuführen und zu etablieren. Die Anforderungen an die linke Hand sind in einem überschaubaren Rahmen gehalten, der zumeist akkordische Klang bedingt jedoch das Liegenlassen einzelner oder weniger Greiffinger. Die dabei entstehende atmosphärische und melodieorientierte Tonsprache lässt Spieler und Zuhörer sicher auch sehr schnell in Gedanken verreisen …

Rainer Schrecklinger

Rainer Schrecklinger,
geb. 1980, studierte Musikpädagogik mit Hauptfach Gitarre bei Michael Koch an der Johannes-Gutenberg-Universität in Mainz und absolvierte ein künstlerisches Aufbaustudium „Gitarre Worldmusic" bei Prof. Thomas Fellow an der Musikhochschule „Carl Maria von Weber" in Dresden.
Er ist Gitarrenlehrer an der Städtischen Musikschule Aschaffenburg und am Peter-Cornelius-Konservatorium der Stadt Mainz. Neben seiner pädagogischen und künstlerischen Tätigkeit schreibt und arrangiert er Gitarrenmusik für Unterricht und Bühne.

On the road
16 Snapshots

After a journey, for a long time we draw on all the memories, experiences, encounters with people and the impressions of fascinating creatures and landscapes. The compositions in this edition are snapshots to listen to. For each of them, I remembered a very specific image, experience or feeling I had during one of my trips, reinterpreting it in sounds.

Furthermore, the pieces are suitable for introducing and establishing the essential three-finger-arpeggios of the right hand. The requirements for the left hand are manageable and most chords only involve holding one or two fingers down. At the same time the resulting sound language, oriented toward the atmosphere and the melody, ensures that the mind of the performer and listener will surely wander quickly…

Rainer Schrecklinger

Rainer Schrecklinger,
Born in 1980, he studied music pedagogy with a specialization in guitar performance with Michael Koch at the Johannes Gutenberg University in Mainz and completed his post-graduate studies in "World Music for Guitar" with Prof. Thomas Fellow at the University of Music "Carl Maria von Weber" in Dresden.
He is a guitar teacher at the Municipal School of Music Aschaffenburg and at the "Peter Cornelius" Conservatory in Mainz. Besides his pedagogical and artistic activities, he writes and arranges music for teaching and performing.

Unterwegs | On the road

Rainer Schrecklinger

1. Tukan | Toucan

(2. x *p* am Griffbrett)

2. Nasenbär | Coati

Edition Ricordi   Sy. 2723   © 2019 by G. Ricordi & C.

3. Blattschneiderameisen I Leaf-cutter ants

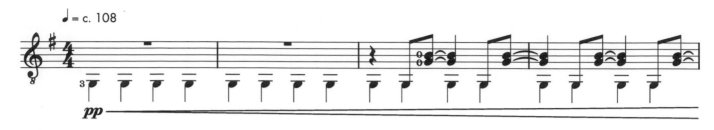

Edition Ricordi Sy. 2723

4. Endless Road

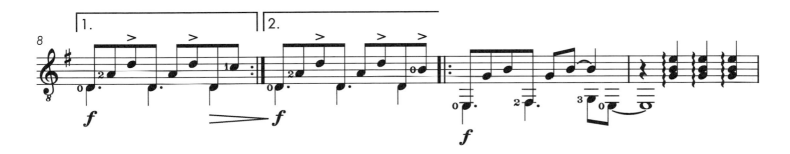

Edition Ricordi

Sy. 2723

5. Herbstlaub I Autumn leaves

6. Der Olivenbaum I The olive tree

7. Das verlassene Haus I The abandoned house

8. Flussabwärts I Down the river

9. Schwerelos I Weightless

10. In der Hängematte | In the hammock

Edition Ricordi   Sy. 2723   © 2019 by G. Ricordi & C.

11. Vollmond | Full moon

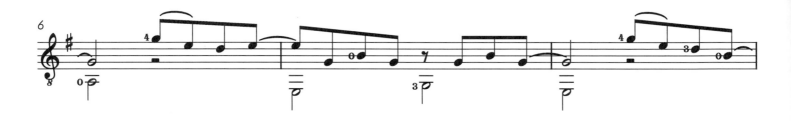

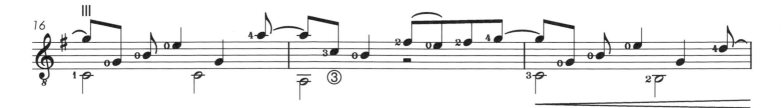

FL. XII

Sy. 2723

12. Was wäre wenn? I What if?

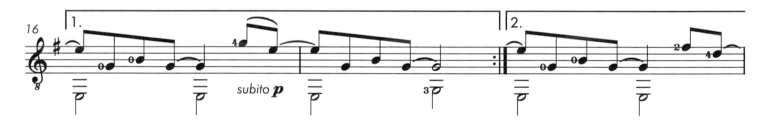

13. Warten auf Regen I Waiting for the rain

14. Blick über den Fjord | A view over the fjord

Sy. 2723

15. Seite an Seite | Side by side

16. Kolibris | Hummingbird

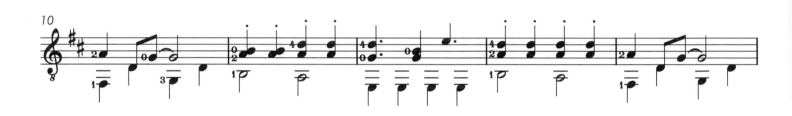